This and that

This family is going on holiday with words which contain the letters **th**.

■ Fit the words in the suitcases into the puzzles.

Mum
other
the
they

Dad
either
their
weather

Bob
another
further
rather

■ Use l**oo**k, (say,) cover, write, check to practise all the words.

_____ _____ _____

_____ _____ _____

_____ _____ _____

_____ _____ _____

Tick here when you have checked your work. ☐

A brush with sh

sh

The answers to this crossword all contain the letters **sh**.
Can you solve the clues?

ACROSS

1. end, complete
3. a place to buy things
4. thinking only about yourself
6. runs quickly
8. when two cars bump
9. pencils write more clearly after you do this
10. shove

DOWN

1. what is new and trendy
2. knights used one to protect themselves
3. large boats
5. a small pillow
7. not stale

■ Use look, (say,) cover, write, check to practise all the words.

Tick here when you have checked your work.

Page 4

Schofield & Sims

New Spellaway
Book 1

Learn to spell . . .

1. look   at the word
2. say   the word
3. cover   the word

} loyally

} an option
4. write   the word

5. check   your spelling

} a place of education

New Spellaway 1

Name

Contents

> Not sure what a word means? Need a helping hand? **Use a dictionary!**

About New Spellaway

New Spellaway is a series of four books which progressively cover Key Stage 2 in Spelling. The puzzles are designed to provide short, fun, educational sessions and to complement the formal teaching of spelling. Positive adult support such as offering help, further explanation or providing a dictionary is invaluable to the student. The series also offers children the opportunity to consolidate each new pattern or concept through the multi-sensory look, (say), cover, write, check approach. Children can be further encouraged to keep their own alphabetical list of words they have learned for their future reference.

© 1997 Schofield & Sims Ltd.

978 07217 0847 8

First printed 1997, reprinted 2001, 2004, 2005, 2007
Printed by Wyndeham Gait Ltd, Grimsby.

Schofield & Sims Ltd,
Huddersfield, England

Tel: 01484 607080 Fax: 01484 606815

Wheels of wh

The words in this puzzle all begin with the letters **wh**.
Unscramble the letters on the tyres to find the **wh** words.

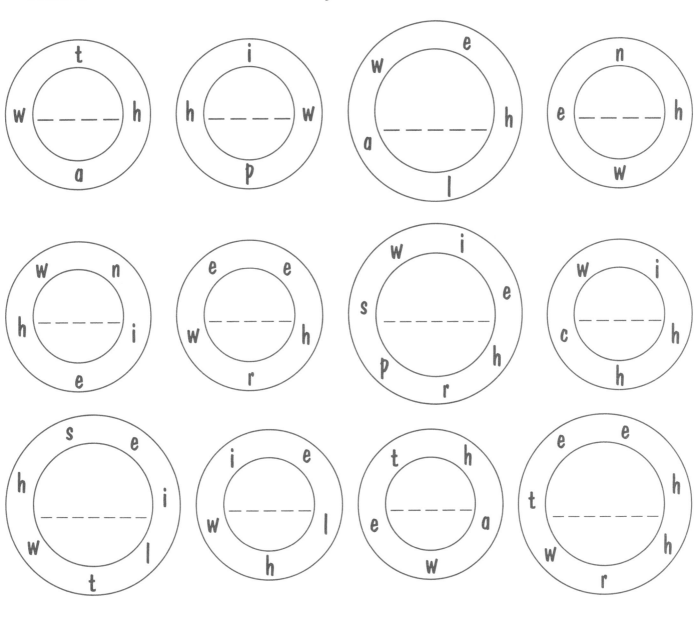

■ Use look, (say,) cover, write, check to practise all the words.

_____ _____ _____

_____ _____ _____

_____ _____ _____

_____ _____ _____

Tick here when you have checked your work. ☐

Cheeky ch

The words in this puzzle have the letters **ch** at the beginning, in the middle or at the end.

■ Fit the words from the box into the correct puzzle.

arch
bunches
charming
cheese
children
choose
coached
couch
munching
ranch
torch
touched

We begin with **ch**.

We end in **ch**.

We have **ch** in the middle.

■ Use l**oo**k, (say,) cover, write, check to practise all the words.

_____   _____   _____

_____   _____   _____

_____   _____   _____

_____   _____   _____

Tick here when you have checked your work. ☐

Hatching and matching

Sometimes we can put two words together to make one new one, so

wind + mill = windmill

■ Join each chicken to an egg to make a new word.

class
card
whirl
brides
loud
tea
motor
book
saw
mouth
week
cart

wind
pot
room
speaker
board
dust
end
maid
case
wheel
way
wash

■ Use look, say, cover, write, check to practise all the words.

Tick here when you have checked your work.

Wily words

English is full of words which can be tricky to spell!

■ Fit the tricky words from the box into the balloons.

aunt	biscuit	friend	saucer	special
beautiful	colour	library	school	was
because	cough	said	scissors	witch

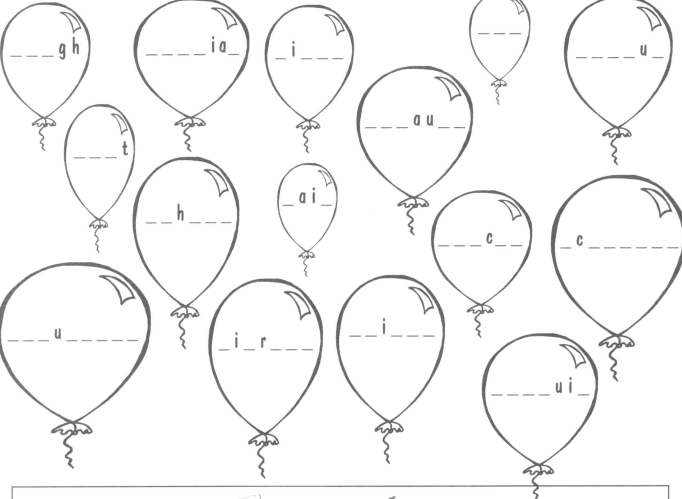

■ Use look, (say,) cover, write, check to practise all the words.

Tick here when you have checked your work.

Fooling with **ee**

The words in this puzzle all contain the letters **ee** or **oo**.

■ Complete each word by adding **ee** or **oo**.
  Then match each word to the correct envelope.

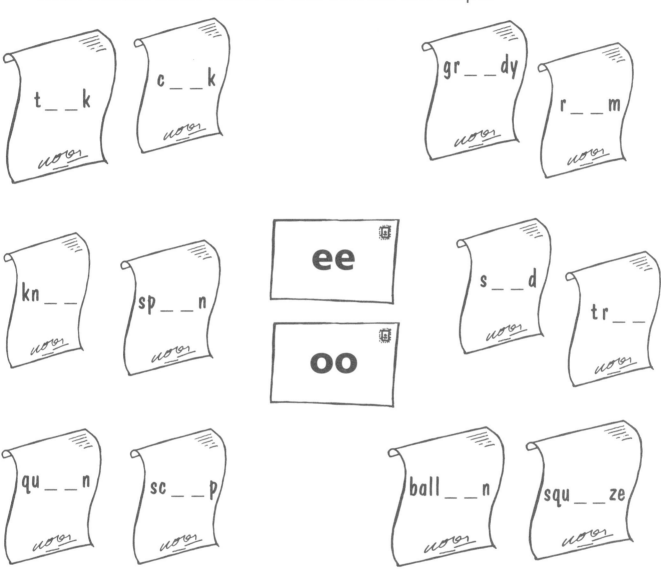

t _ _ k

c _ _ k

gr _ _ dy

r _ _ m

kn _ _

sp _ _ n

ee

oo

s _ _ d

t r _ _

qu _ _ n

sc _ _ p

ball _ _ n

squ _ _ ze

■ Use look, (say,) cover, write, check to practise each word.

_____   _____   _____

_____   _____   _____

_____   _____   _____

_____

Tick here when you have checked your work. ☐

Wandering **wa**

wa as **wǒ**

When **a** comes after **w** it often makes the sound **o**,
e.g. w<u>a</u>s, w<u>a</u>rm, sw<u>a</u>n.

■ The letters **wa** have been missed out of these words.
Fit **wa** back again and write out the completed words.

1 nted _____

2 sp _____

3 rning _____

4 rt _____

5 ffle _____

6 shing _____

7 srm _____

8 llaby _____

9 lking _____

10 sllow _____

11 r _____

12 ddle _____

■ Find and circle the completed words hidden in this ribbon.
One is done for you.

■ Use l👁👁k, (say,) cover, write, che✓k to practise each word.

_____   _____   _____

_____   _____   _____

_____   _____   _____

_____   _____   _____

Tick here when you have checked your work. ☐

Sneaky ea

Rhyming words are words which end with the same sound.

All the rhyming words in this puzzle have the letters **ea** in them.

In these words **ea** makes a sound like **ee**.

Say them all and listen to the sounds.

■ Copy the rhymes from the carrots into the correct hutch.

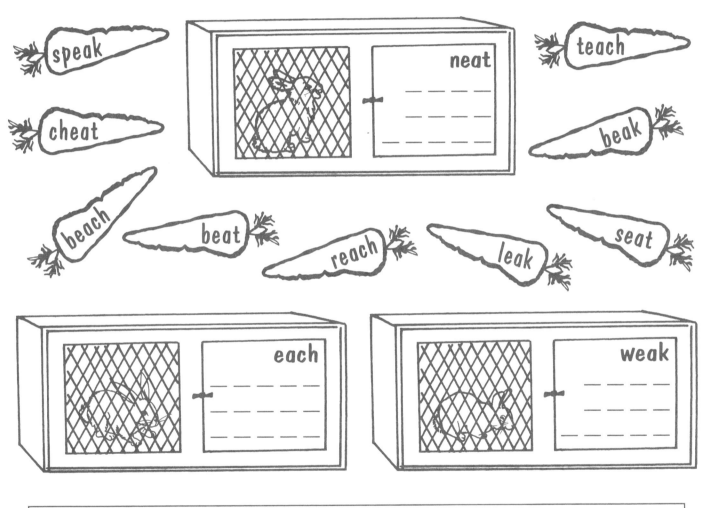

■ Use look, say, cover, write, check to practise all the words.

_____   _____   _____

_____   _____   _____

_____   _____   _____

_____   _____   _____

Tick here when you have checked your work. ☐

Shoals of oa

When the vowels **o** and **a** are put next to each other they can make an **o** sound, e.g. <u>oa</u>k, f<u>oa</u>l, l<u>oa</u>f.

■ Each fish is hiding an **oa** word. Unscramble the letters and write the **oa** words in the boat.

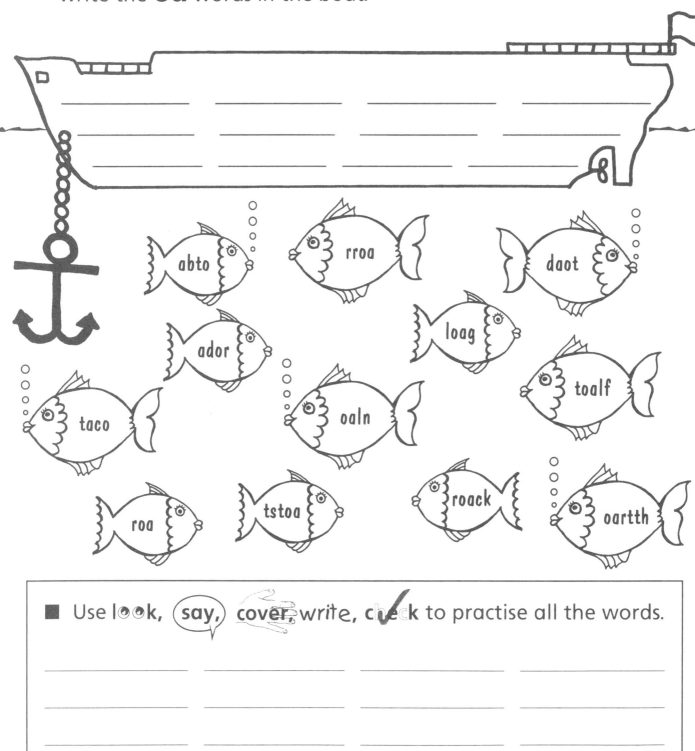

abto · rroa · daot · loag · ador · taco · oaln · toalf · roa · tstoa · roack · oartth

■ Use look, (say,) cover, write, check to practise all the words.

Tick here when you have checked your work.

Chain of **ai**

When the vowels **a** and **i** are put next to each other, they make an **ay** sound, e.g. r<u>ai</u>n, n<u>ai</u>l, <u>ai</u>d.

■ The letters **ai** have been missed out of these words. Put them back and write out the whole word.

1 rnbow _____

2 trn _____

3 chn _____

4 rlway _____

5 afrd _____

6 wt _____

7 pd _____

8 pnt _____

9 remn _____

10 compln _____

11 entertn _____

12 strght _____

■ Find and circle the completed words hidden in this ribbon. One is done for you.

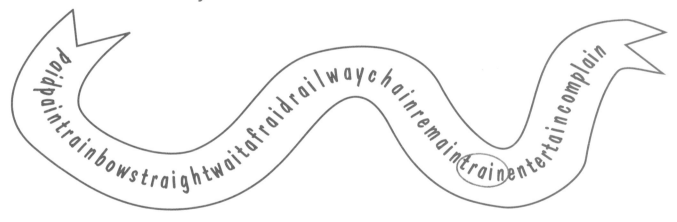

■ Use lo⊙k, (say,) cover, write, ch⊘ck to practise all the words.

_____ _____ _____

_____ _____ _____

_____ _____ _____

_____ _____ _____

Tick here when you have checked your work. ☐

Joining **oi**

When the vowels **o** and **i** are put next to each other they can make an **oy** sound, e.g. s<u>oi</u>l, j<u>oi</u>n, <u>oi</u>nk.

■ The **oi** words in this puzzle all have a rhyming partner hidden somewhere on the footprints. Join the rhyming pairs together.

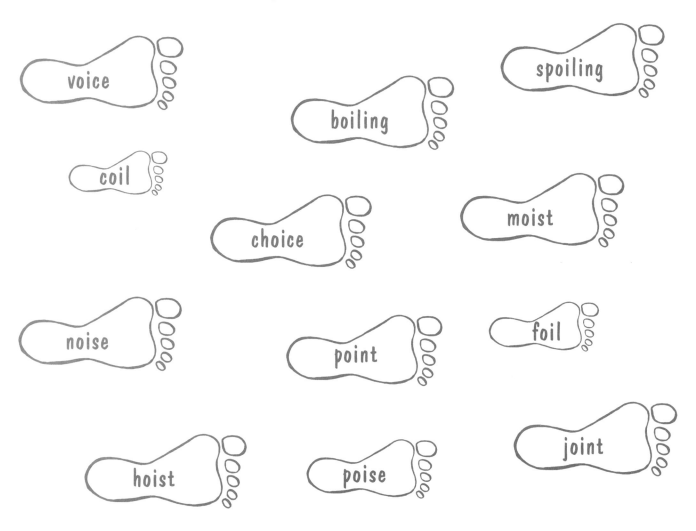

■ Use look, (say,) cover, write, check to practise all the words.

_____   _____   _____

_____   _____   _____

_____   _____   _____

_____   _____   _____

Tick here when you have checked your work. ☐

A shield of **ie**

When the vowels **i** and **e** are put next to each other they can make an **ee** sound, e.g. sh**ie**ld, p**ie**r.

■ Add **ie** to each set of letters to make a word. Fit the completed words onto the shield.

1 fld _____

2 yld _____

3 pce _____

4 nce _____

5 prst _____

6 prce _____

7 belve _____

8 achve _____

9 shrk _____

10 grf _____

11 brf _____

12 sge _____

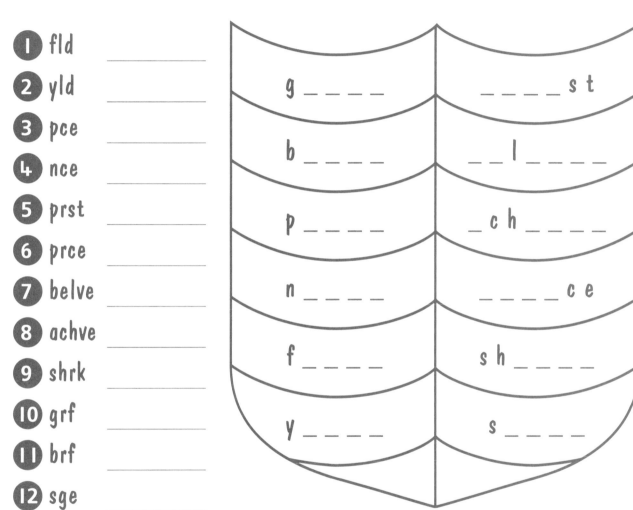

g _ _ _ _ _   _ _ _ _ _ s t

b _ _ _ _   _ _ l _ _ _ _

p _ _ _ _   _ c h _ _ _ _

n _ _ _ _   _ _ _ _ c e

f _ _ _ _   s h _ _ _ _

y _ _ _ _   s _ _ _ _

■ Use l**oo**k, (say,) cover, write, ch**e**ck to practise all the words.

_____ _____ _____

_____ _____ _____

_____ _____ _____

Tick here when you have checked your work. ☐

Time travel

■ Fit the names of the months into the seasons.

Spring

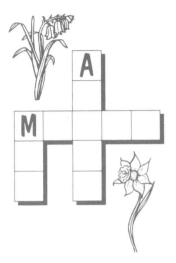

Autumn

January
February
March
April
May
June
July
August
September
October
November
December

Summer

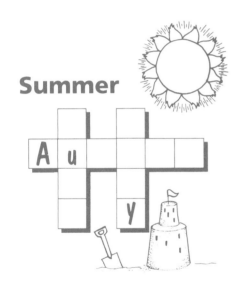

Winter

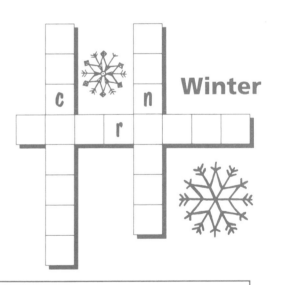

■ Use look, (say,) cover, write, check to practise all the words.

Tick here when you have checked your work.

New Spellaway 1

Key Stage 2

Answers

About New Spellaway

New Spellaway is a series of four books which progressively cover Key Stage 2 in Spelling. The puzzles are designed to provide short, fun, educational sessions and to complement the formal teaching of spelling. Positive adult support such as offering help, further explanation or providing a dictionary is invaluable to the student. The series also offers children the opportunity to consolidate each new pattern or concept through the multi-sensory look, (say,) cover write, check approach. Children can be further encouraged to keep their own alphabetical list of words they have learned for their future reference.

You may wish to separate this answer section from the questions. Carefully pull out the middle 8 pages, then push the wire stitching back into place.

This and that

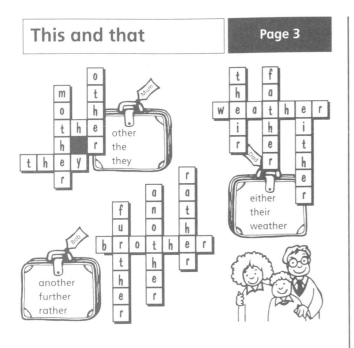

A brush with sh

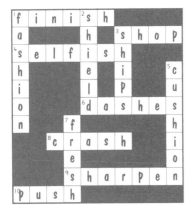

Wheels of wh

Cheeky ch

arch
bunches
charming
cheese
children
choose
coached
couch
munching
ranch
torch
touched

We begin with ch.

We end in ch.

We have ch in the middle.

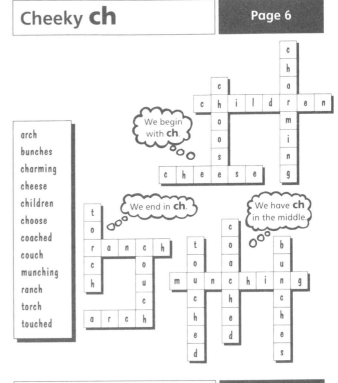

Hatching and matching

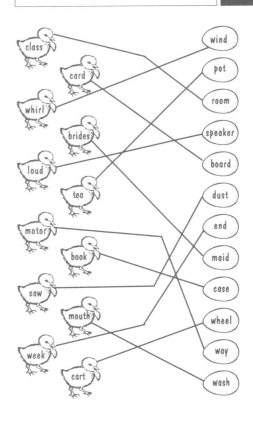

classroom
cardboard
whirlwind
bridesmaid
loudspeaker
teapot
motorway
bookcase
sawdust
mouthwash
weekend
cartwheel

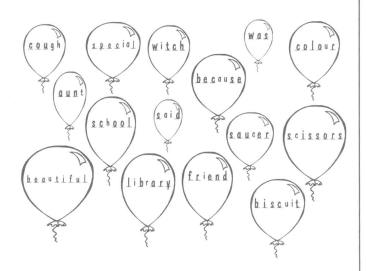

cough, special, witch, was, colour, aunt, because, school, said, saucer, scissors, beautiful, library, friend, biscuit

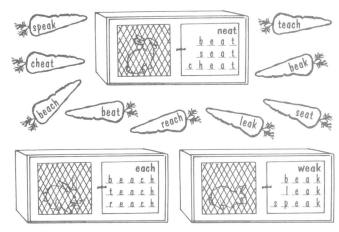

speak, teach, cheat, beak, beach, beat, reach, leak, seat

neat
b e a t
s e a t
c h e a t

each
b e a c h
t e a c h
r e a c h

weak
b e a k
l e a k
s p e a k

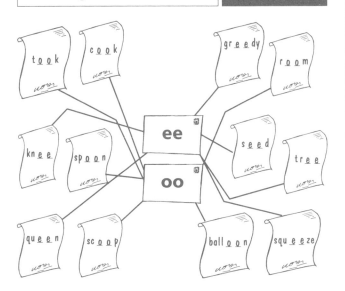

took, cook, greedy, room, knee, spoon, seed, tree, queen, scoop, balloon, squeeze

ee
oo

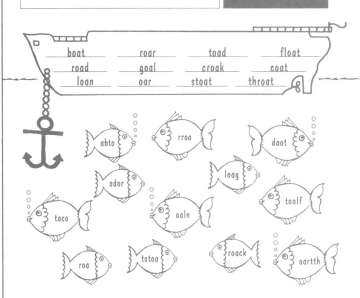

boat — roar — toad — float
road — goal — croak — coat
loan — oar — stoat — throat

abto, rroa, daot, ador, loag, toalf, taco, oaln, roa, tstoa, roack, oartth

1. nted — wanted
2. sp — wasp
3. rning — warning
4. rt — wart
5. ffle — waffle
6. shing — washing
7. srm — swarm
8. llaby — wallaby
9. lking — walking
10. sllow — swallow
11. r — war
12. ddle — waddle

Chain of **ai** | Page 13

1. rnbow — rainbow
2. trn — train
3. chn — chain
4. rlway — railway
5. afrd — afraid
6. wt — wait
7. pd — paid
8. pnt — paint
9. remn — remain
10. compln — complain
11. entertn — entertain
12. strght — straight

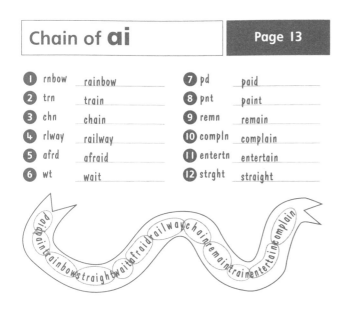

Time travel | Page 16

Spring
Summer

January
February
March
April
May
June
July
August
September
October
November
December

Autumn
Winter

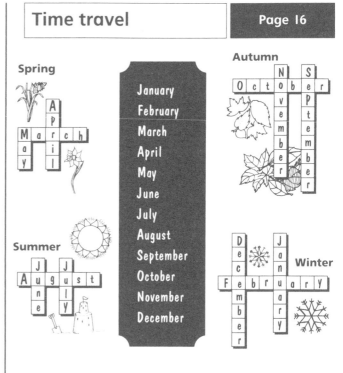

Joining **oi** | Page 14

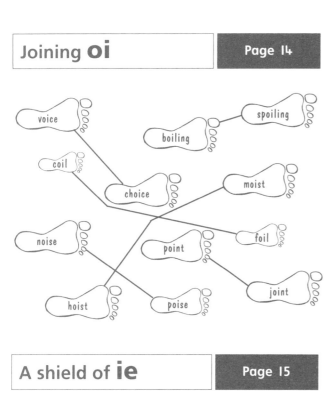

voice, spoiling, boiling, coil, choice, moist, noise, point, foil, hoist, poise, joint

A snake of **a_e** | Page 17

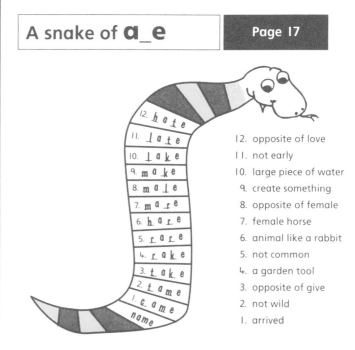

12. h a t e — opposite of love
11. l a t e — not early
10. l a k e — large piece of water
9. m a k e — create something
8. m a l e — opposite of female
7. m a r e — female horse
6. h a r e — animal like a rabbit
5. r a r e — not common
4. r a k e — a garden tool
3. t a k e — opposite of give
2. t a m e — not wild
1. c a m e — arrived

name

A shield of **ie** | Page 15

field
yield
piece
niece
priest
pierce
believe
achieve
shriek
grief
brief
siege

grief priest
brief believe
piece achieve
niece pierce
field shriek
yield siege

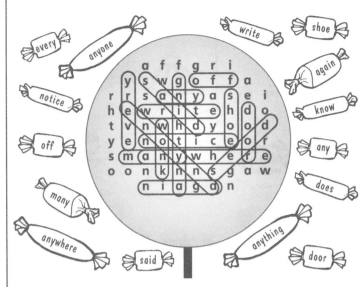

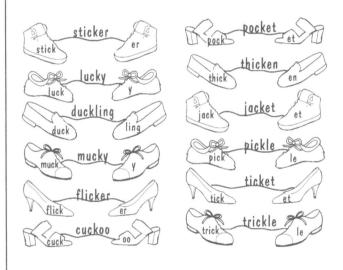

d u n e	• a low hill of sand
t u n e	• melody
t u b e	• pipe
c u b e	• a solid shape
c u r e	• make someone better
p u r e	• totally clean
s u r e	• certain
l u r e	• tempt
l u t e	• old-fashioned instrument
m u t e	• unable to speak
m u l e	• animal like a donkey
r u l e	• a law, regulation
r u d e	

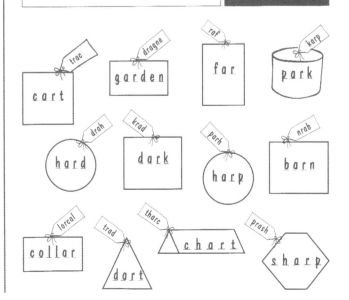

Answer page 5

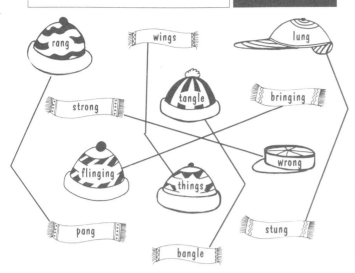

one — sixteen
two — seventeen
three — eighteen
four — nineteen
five — twenty
six — thirty
seven — forty
eight — fifty
nine — sixty
ten — seventy
eleven — eighty
twelve — ninety
thirteen — hundred
fourteen — thousand
fifteen — million

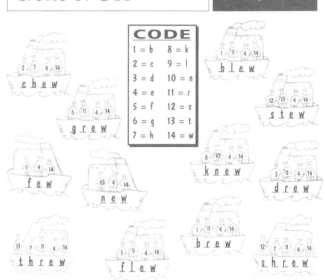

Some words may be found in more than one place.

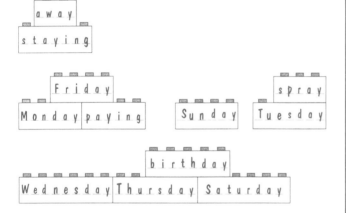

away
staying
Friday
Monday   paying
Sunday
spray
Tuesday
birthday
Wednesday   Thursday   Saturday

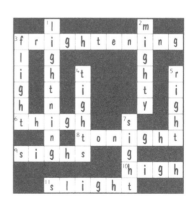

CODE
1 = b   8 = k
2 = c   9 = l
3 = d   10 = n
4 = e   11 = r
5 = f   12 = s
6 = g   13 = t
7 = h   14 = w

chew   blew   grew   stew
few   knew   new   drew
threw   brew   flew   shrew

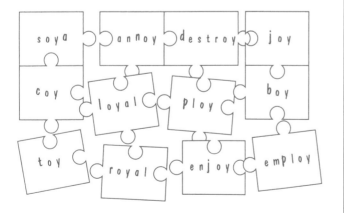

soya   annoy   destroy   joy
coy   loyal   ploy   boy
toy   royal   enjoy   employ

frightening
lightning
mighty
light
tiny
righ
thigh
tonight
sighs
high
slight

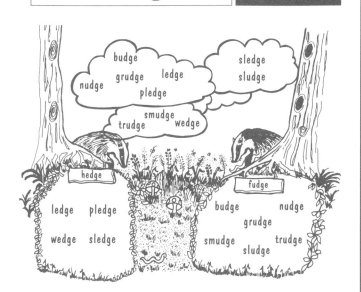

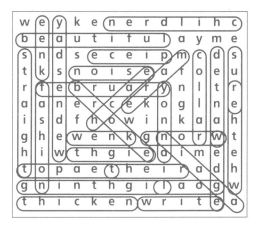

Answer page 7

New Spellaway 1

Key Stage 2

Answers

A snake of a_e

Adding magic **e** to a word changes the sound of the vowel, e.g. t<u>a</u>p changes to t<u>a</u>p<u>e</u>.

■ Climb the **a_e** snake.
Begin at the first
word then change
just one letter at
a time. The clues
will help you!

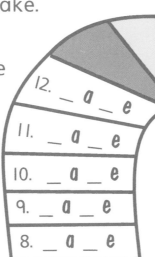

12. _ a _ e
11. _ a _ e
10. _ a _ e
9. _ a _ e
8. _ a _ e
7. _ a _ e
6. _ a _ e
5. _ a _ e
4. _ a _ e
3. _ a _ e
2. _ a _ e
1. _ a _ e
name

12. opposite of love

11. not early

10. large piece of water

9. create something

8. opposite of female

7. female horse

6. animal like a rabbit

5. not common

4. a garden tool

3. opposite of give

2. not wild

1. arrived

■ Use look, (say,) cover, write, check to practise all the words.

_____   _____   _____

_____   _____   _____

_____   _____   _____

Tick here when you have checked your work. ☐

A hive of i_e

Adding magic **e** to a word changes the sound of the vowel,
e.g. s**i**t changes to s**i**t**e**.

■ The bees are collecting letters to add to **i_e**.
Write the words they make in the honeycomb.

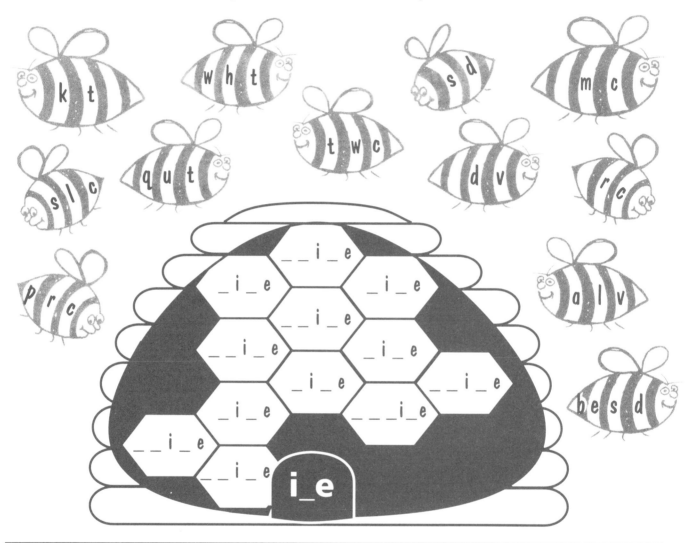

■ Use look, say, cover, write, check to practise all the words.

_____   _____   _____

_____   _____   _____

_____   _____   _____

_____   _____

Tick here when you have checked your work. ☐

Close to o_e

Adding magic **e** to a word changes the sound of a vowel, e.g. **n_o_t** changes to **n_o_te**.

■ Join the rhyming **o_e** words.

■ Use l**oo**k, (say,) cover, write, check to practise all the words.

_____   _____   _____

_____   _____   _____

_____   _____   _____

_____   _____   _____

Tick here when you have checked your work. ☐

u_e adventure

Adding magic **e** to a word changes the sound of the vowel, e.g. **cut** changes to **cute**.

■ Climb the **u_e** ladder to escape from the dragon. Begin at the first word and change just one letter each time you climb! The clues will help you.

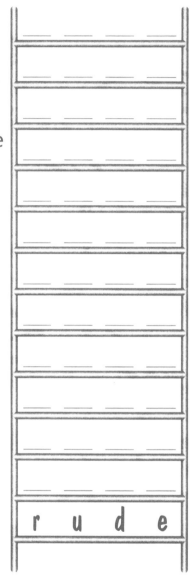

r u d e

• a low hill of sand

• melody

• pipe

• a solid shape

• make someone better

• totally clean

• certain

• tempt

• old-fashioned instrument

• unable to speak

• animal like a donkey

• a law, regulation

■ Use look, (say,) cover, write, check to practise all the words.

Tick here when you have checked your work.

Sticky spellings

Lots of words can be tricky to spell!

■ Can you find the words on the sweets hidden in the lollipop? They are written forwards, backwards, up, down and diagonally!

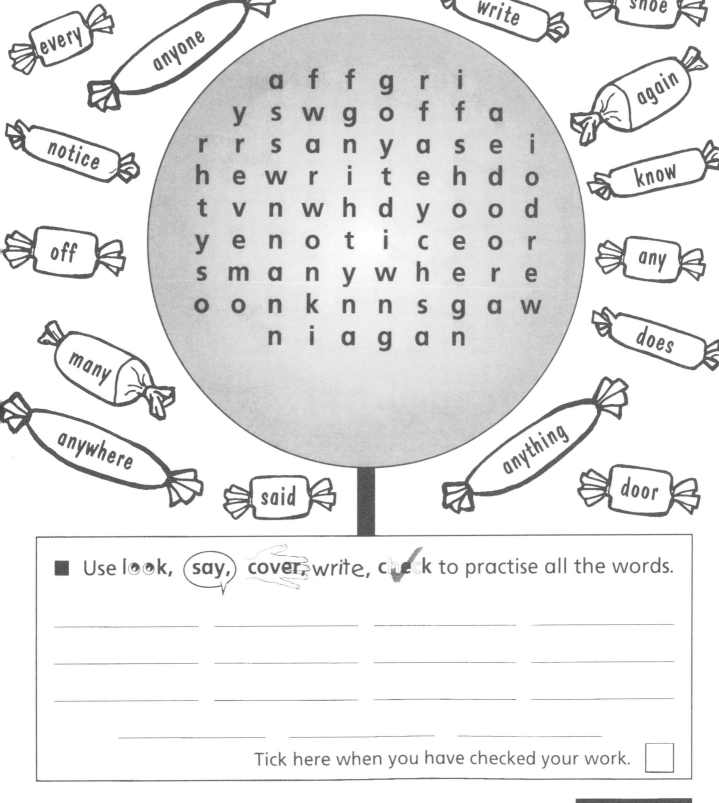

every anyone write shoe again notice know off any

a f f g r i
y s w g o f f a
r r s a n y a s e i
h e w r i t e h d o
t v n w h d y o o d
y e n o t i c e o r
s m a n y w h e r e
o o n k n n s g a w
n i a g a n

does many anywhere said anything door

■ Use l**oo**k, (say,) **cover** write, ch**eck** to practise all the words.

_____   _____   _____   _____

_____   _____   _____   _____

_____   _____   _____   _____

Tick here when you have checked your work. ☐

Stuck on **ck**

Some words use **c** and **k** together to make a **c** sound,
e.g. ne<u>ck</u>, clo<u>ck</u>, ti<u>ck</u>le.

■ Each shoe has one part of a **ck** word on it.
Read both shoes and write the completed word on each
shoelace.

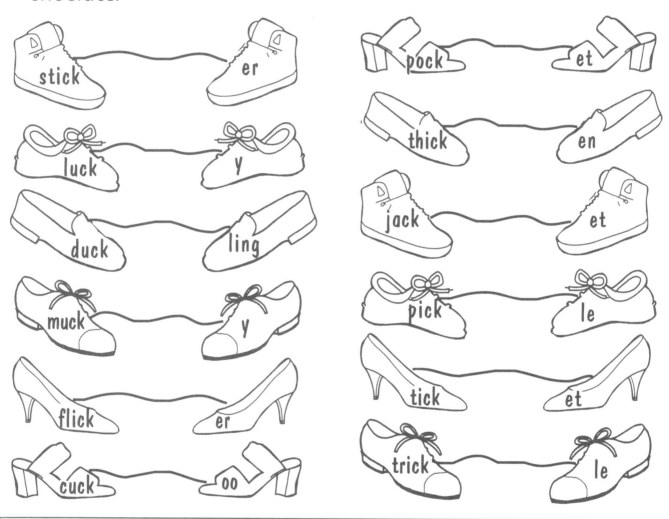

■ Use look, (say,) cover, write, check to practise all the words.

_____ _____ _____

_____ _____ _____

_____ _____ _____

Tick here when you have checked your work. ☐

Parcels of **ar**

ar

The words in this puzzle all contain the letters **ar**.

■ Unscramble the letters on the labels to find the **ar** words for each parcel.

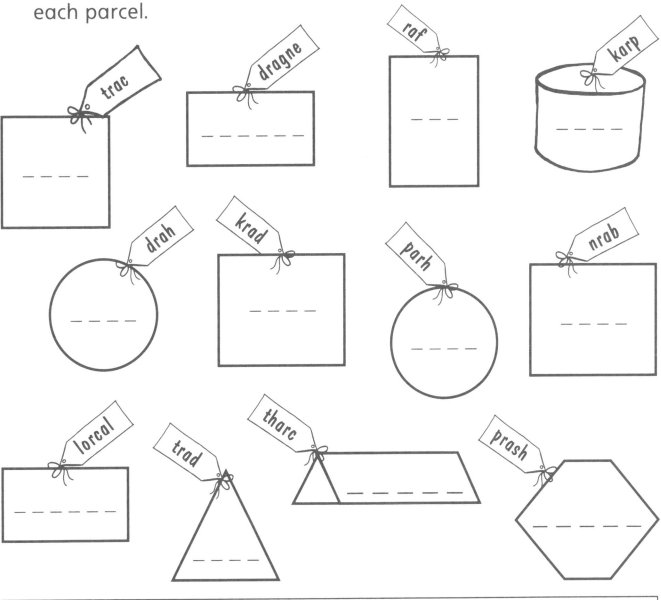

Sing, song, sang, sung

ing, ong, ang, ung

The words in this puzzle all contain the letters **ing**, **ong**, **ang** or **ung**.

■ Join the rhyming words.

rang

wings

lung

strong

tangle

bringing

flinging

things

wrong

pang

stung

bangle

■ Use look, say, cover, write, check to practise all the words.

Tick here when you have checked your work.

Playing with **ay**

The words in this puzzle all contain the letters **ay** somewhere in them.

■ Fit one word from the toybox into each brick.

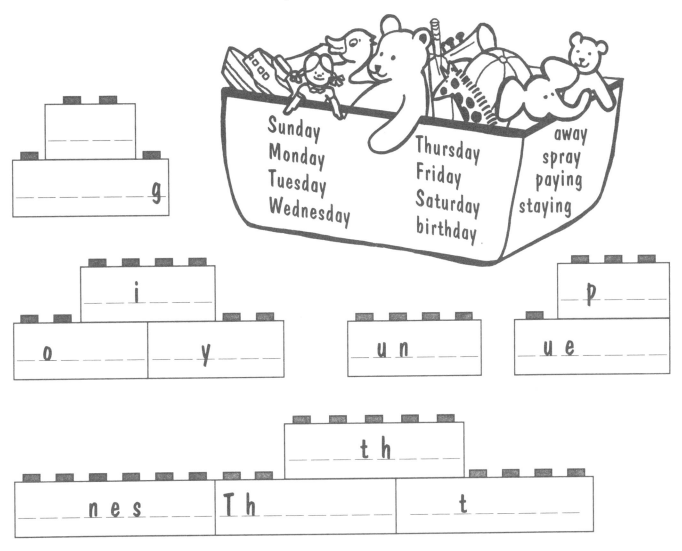

Sunday
Monday
Tuesday
Wednesday

Thursday
Friday
Saturday
birthday

away
spray
paying
staying

_ _ _ _ _ _ g

_ _ i _ _ _

_ o _ _ _

_ _ y _ _ _

_ _ u n _ _ _

_ _ _ p _ _ _

_ u e _ _ _

_ _ _ t h _ _ _

_ _ n e s _ _ _

T h _ _ _ _ _ _

_ _ t _ _ _ _ _

■ Use look, (say,) cover, write, check to practise all the words.

_____ _____ _____

_____ _____ _____

_____ _____ _____

Tick here when you have checked your work. ☐

Toying with **oy**

oy

The words in the puzzle all include the letters **oy**.

- Can you fit one word from the box on to each piece of the jigsaw?

annoy	destroy	joy	royal
boy	employ	loyal	soya
coy	enjoy	ploy	toy

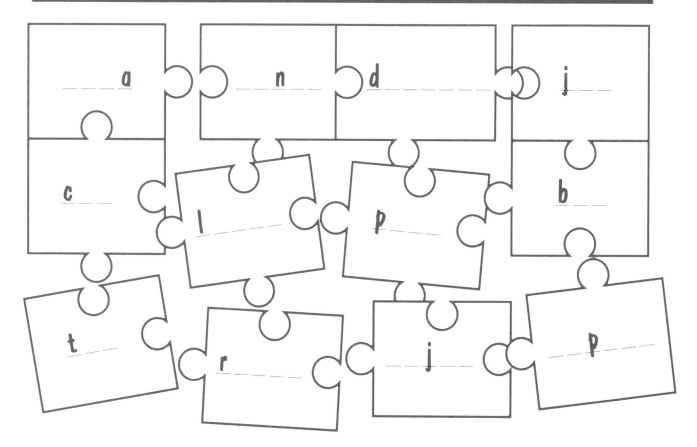

- Use look, (say,) cover, write, check to practise all the words.

_____ _____ _____

_____ _____ _____

_____ _____ _____

Tick here when you have checked your work. ☐

Number Nightmare

■ All the numbers are hidden in the wordsearch.
They are written forwards, backwards, up, down and diagonally!
Can you find them all?

one	sixteen
two	seventeen
three	eighteen
four	nineteen
five	twenty
six	thirty
seven	forty
eight	fifty
nine	sixty
ten	seventy
eleven	eighty
twelve	ninety
thirteen	hundred
fourteen	thousand
fifteen	million

```
e  f  n  e  e  t  n  e  v  e  s
s  o  n  e  e  t  r  u  o  f  i
e  r  f  t  w  e  n  t  y  i  x
v  t  x  e  s  e  v  e  n  f  t
e  y  n  i  n  e  i  g  h  t  e
n  y  x  g  w  r  g  a  i  e  e
t  t  u  h  r  u  h  r  g  e  n
y  r  t  t  h  o  u  s  a  n  d
t  i  h  e  w  f  n  t  y  s  y
f  h  r  e  r  o  d  e  t  u  t
i  t  e  n  i  w  r  w  h  o  e
f  e  e  l  e  v  e  n  g  h  n
e  v  l  e  w  t  d  a  i  t  i
s  i  x  t  h  i  r  t  e  e  n
m  f  i  n  e  e  t  e  n  i  n
```

■ Use look, (say,) cover, write, check to practise the underlined words.

_____   _____   _____

_____   _____   _____

_____   _____   _____

Tick here when you have checked your work. ☐

Crews of **ew**

Usually the letters **ew** make an **oo** sound, e.g. scr<u>ew</u>, p<u>ew</u>, n<u>ew</u>t.

■ Use the code in the box and the numbers on the crews' shirts to discover the name of each boat. Their names all contain the letters **ew**.

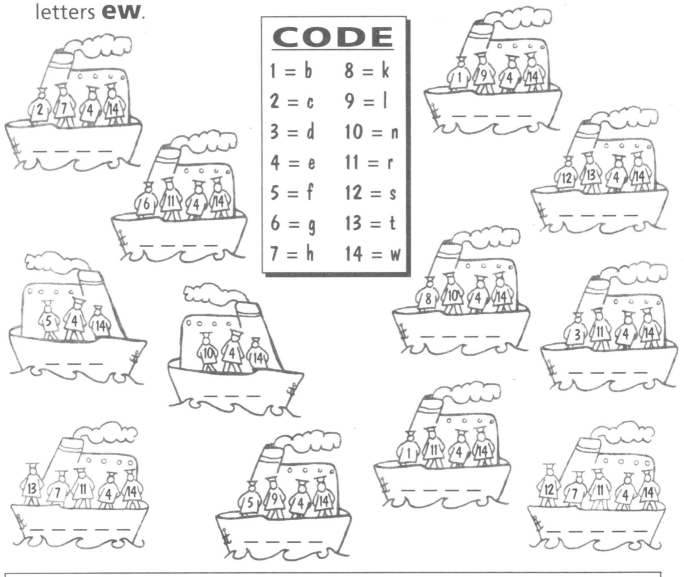

CODE

1 = b	8 = k
2 = c	9 = l
3 = d	10 = n
4 = e	11 = r
5 = f	12 = s
6 = g	13 = t
7 = h	14 = w

■ Use l**oo**k, (say,) cover, write, check to practise each word.

_____   _____   _____

_____   _____   _____

_____   _____   _____

_____   _____   _____

Tick here when you have checked your work. ☐

Frightful **igh**

igh as Ī

When the three letters **igh** come next to each other they usually make an **i** sound, e.g. n<u>igh</u>t, l<u>igh</u>t, fr<u>igh</u>t.

■ The answers to this crossword all contain the letters **igh**. Can you solve the clues?

ACROSS

3. Scary
6. Top part of leg
8. This evening
9. Breathes out deeply
10. Not low
11. Small, slim

DOWN

1. Thunder and _____
2. Strong, powerful
3. A journey in the air
4. An item of clothing for legs
5. Opposite of left
7. The ability to see

■ Use look, (say,) cover, write, check to practise all the words.

_____ _____ _____

_____ _____ _____

_____ _____ _____

Tick here when you have checked your work. ☐

Badgering **dge**

dge

These badgers are collecting **dge** words but they only want words which rhyme with the names of their houses!

■ Write the words from the clouds into the correct set.

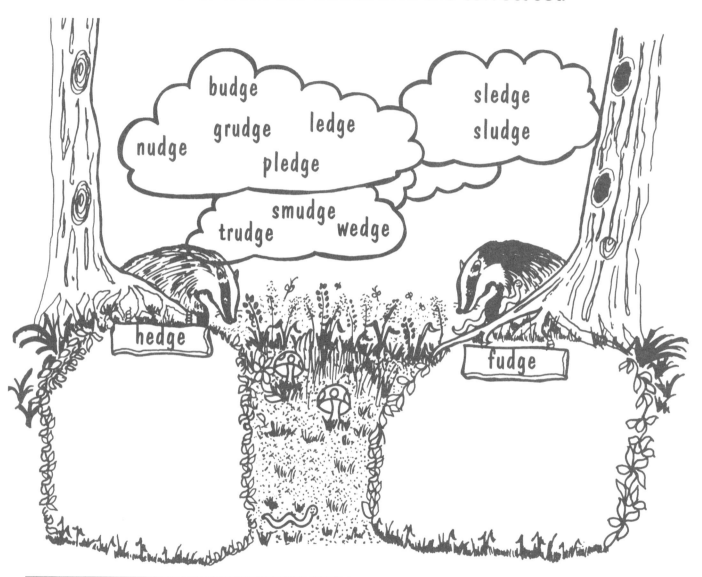

budge

grudge   ledge

nudge   pledge

sledge

sludge

smudge   wedge

trudge

hedge

fudge

■ Use l**oo**k, (say,) cover, write, check to practise each word.

_____   _____   _____

_____   _____   _____

_____   _____   _____

Tick here when you have checked your work. ☐

Megapuzzle

This wordsearch is hiding one word from every puzzle in this book. Can you find them all?

again

annoy

beautiful

broke

children

collar

each

eight

fashion

February

goal

knee

knew

w	e	y	k	e	n	e	r	d	l	i	h	c
b	e	a	u	t	i	f	u	l	a	y	m	e
s	n	d	s	e	c	e	i	p	m	c	d	s
t	k	s	n	o	i	s	e	a	f	o	e	u
r	f	e	b	r	u	a	r	y	n	l	t	r
a	a	n	e	r	c	e	k	o	g	l	n	e
i	s	d	f	h	o	w	i	n	k	a	a	h
g	h	e	w	e	n	k	g	n	o	r	w	t
h	i	w	t	h	g	i	e	a	i	m	e	e
t	o	p	a	e	t	h	e	i	r	a	d	h
g	n	i	n	t	h	g	i	l	a	o	g	w
t	h	i	c	k	e	n	w	r	i	t	e	a

lightning

mare

noise

piece

straight

sure

teapot

their

thicken

wanted

wedge

Wednesday

whether

write

wrong

Congratulations, you have finished this workbook!

Schofield&Sims

Schofield & Sims
HELPING CHILDREN TO LEARN

Schofield and Sims have, for over a hundred years, published a wide variety of educational materials for use in schools or at home. Specialising in products for Early Years, Key Stage 1 and Key Stage 2, our texts are written by experienced teachers and concentrate on the key areas of Maths, English and Science. The range includes workbooks, revision guides, practice papers, dictionaries and laminated posters.

New Spellaway Book 1

A progressive series of four workbooks complementing the formal teaching of spelling through puzzles designed to provide short, fun, educational sessions. New patterns are consolidated through the multi-sensory 'look, say, cover, write, check' approach.

New Spellaway Book 1 - 978 07217 0847 8   New Spellaway Book 3 - 978 07217 0849 2
New Spellaway Book 2 - 978 07217 0848 5   New Spellaway Book 4 - 978 07217 0850 8

Some of our other Key Stage 2 English materials include:

NEW **Understanding English** – a series of eight learning workbooks, designed to help children to understand and learn the main areas of English at Key Stage 2.

NEW **Revision Guide and Practice Papers at Key Stage 2** – a clear and comprehensive explanation is given of every topic likely to be covered in the Key Stage test. All the topics are linked to the curriculum with the links displayed in an easy to read curriculum chart. Practice Papers are similar in both appearance and content to the actual test. Each page is cross referenced to the Revision Guide.

Posters
• Famous Writers   • William Shakespeare   • Charles Dickens

Available in most bookshops and many libraries or contact us for more information and a free catalogue:

• Telephone us on 01484 607080
• By sending us a fax on 01484 606815
• E-mail us on sales@schofieldandsims.co.uk
• Direct from our Website www.schofieldandsims.co.uk

Our customer service team will be happy to help with your enquiry

Schofield & Sims
HELPING CHILDREN TO LEARN

Dogley Mill, Fenay Bridge, Huddersfield HD8 0NQ
Phone 01484 607080 Facsimile 01484 606815

ISBN 978-07217-0847-8

9 780721 708478

£1.95
Key Stage 2
Age range 7-11 years